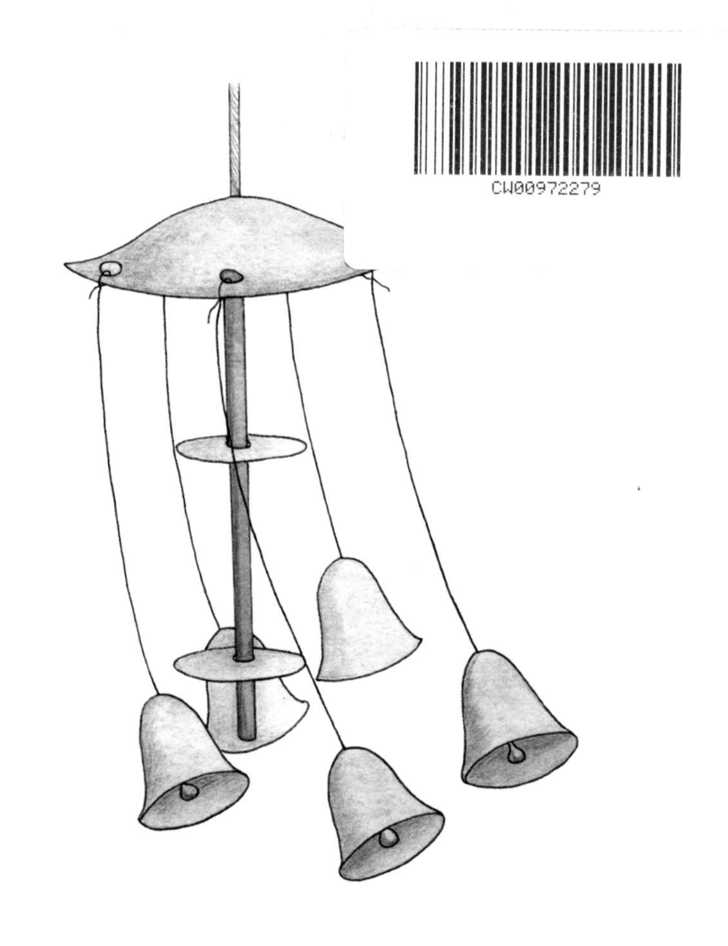

Ting-a-ling-a-ling.
Ring the bells in the wind.

Ring-a-ding-a-ding. Lotty pulls the string.

Ding-dong, ding-dong.
The bells ring.
Ding-dong.

Bing-bong, bing-bong.

Bang the gong.

BONG.

Zing, zing, zing, zing.
The bees are buzzing.
Zzzzz ... zzzzz ...zzzzz.

Ping-pong, ping-pong.
The dogs pull .....
PING!

Bang, clang, bang, clang. Bang the pans. CLANG!

Sing, song, sing, sing, song. Sing along with the song.